STRANGER THINGS

THE UNOFFICIAL COLOURING BOOK

SparkPool

Published in 2023
First published in the UK by SparkPool Publishing
An imprint of Igloo Books Ltd
Cottage Farm, NN6 0BJ, UK
Owned by Bonnier Books
Sveavägen 56, Stockholm, Sweden
www.igloobooks.com

0723 003
2 4 6 8 10 9 7 5 3
ISBN 978-1-83771-170-3

Illustrated by Maurizio Campidelli
Designed by Simon Parker
Edited by Alexandra Chapman

Printed and manufactured in China

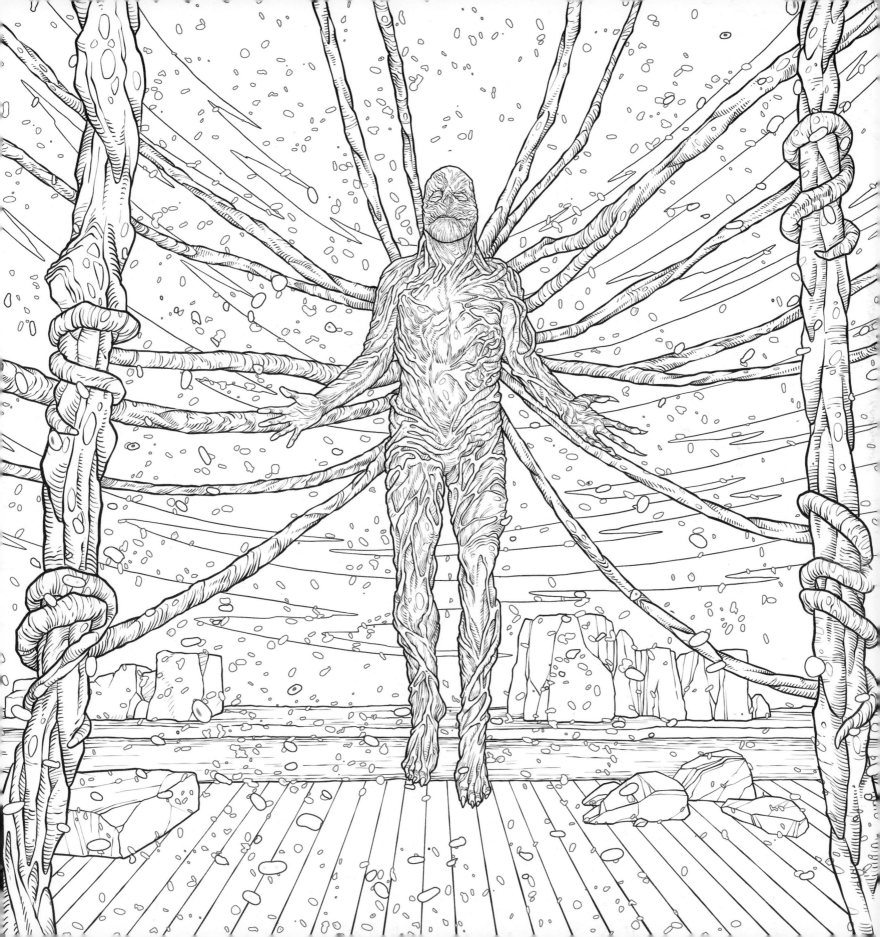